VARIETY

IN

MATHEMATICS

LESSONS

Association of Teachers of Mathematics

Published by Association of Teachers of Mathematics
Unit 7 Prime Industrial Park, Shaftesbury Street, Derby DE23 8YB

Telephone: 01332 346599
Fax: 01332 204357
Email: admin@atm.org.uk
Website: www.atm.org.uk

ISBN 978-1-898611-54-7

© Colin Foster, 2008

Colin Foster teaches mathematics at an 11-18 school in Coventry.

I would like to thank the Publications Group for all their work getting this book ready, Gill Othen for very helpful comments on the text, and Charlotte Blore (a member of my tutor group) for drawing some of the pictures. Most of all, I am grateful to the many learners who have given their energy to the various tasks in this book, particularly those whose work is included.

Design by David Cutting, DCG DESIGN

Drawings on pages 6, 30 and 32 © Charlotte Blore, 2007
Cover drawings by (clockwise from the top) Elizabeth, Suman, George, Sam and Pamelbir

Photographs on page 30 © Julian Beever, 2006

Contents

Introduction

This book arose from comments made by school pupils that lessons in other subjects often feel more varied than those in mathematics. In English lessons, for example, activities might regularly include:

◆ creative writing, either individually or collaboratively

◆ improvisation or performance in the drama studio

◆ whole-class or individual reading of plays, novels, poems and short stories

◆ watching films, documentaries and televised plays and novels

◆ formal and informal debates

◆ whole-class or group discussions

◆ analysis of somebody else's writing

◆ exercises on spelling, grammar or punctuation

For a lot of students it seems that too many mathematics lessons feel like the last item on the list. To them the lessons appear dry, predictable, routine and uninspiring. Yet there is no need for mathematics to be experienced in such a dull manner, as there are countless more imaginative ways of structuring mathematics lessons.

Variety in Mathematics Lessons collects together some more interesting lesson models. Although the book includes examples of lessons, it is not merely a set of lesson plans. In a way, it focuses on the stage *before* a lesson plan is formed – more like *a plan for a lesson plan*.

Nothing here should be taken as prescriptive. Professionals in their particular classrooms are the only people who are in the position to know their learners. Only they can take account of the many factors concerning the pupils and their teacher at a given moment. This book offers a collection of rough 'templates' for different genres of mathematics lesson. If things are feeling a bit samey, it might be time for a different 'sort' of lesson, regardless of the subject matter you wish to work on. This book focuses on particular lesson models that have been enjoyable to teach, but it is not by any means meant to be a comprehensive catalogue of lesson types.

There are often strong pressures on teachers towards consistency, confining lessons to predetermined moulds. This is felt to provide a safe and comfortable structure for both learners and teachers, yet can lead to an uninspiring uniformity. It is far better to aim for surprise, flexibility, diversity and variety in mathematics lessons.

 The main idea for each lesson is introduced with the light bulb icon.

 Dealing with the aftermath – the follow-up to the main thrust of the lesson – is identified by the footprints.

 Further avenues that can be explored and extensions of the main idea are in tinted boxes with the arrow icon.

Something weird to resolve

This type of lesson begins with something which does not make sense; a starting point that everyone can see is strange, unexpected, problematic, unreasonable or apparently impossible.

Many so-called 'maths problems' are not noticeably *problematic* or troublesome by their nature; just tedious. For this kind of lesson, you need a beginning that creates enough energy in the learner to lead them to desire resolution – this is where the weird, twisty or freaky aspect is crucial.

For this phase, it is necessary that

◆ the learners recognise *and feel* the weirdness;

◆ the teacher avoids 'explaining' what is weird as this is about as effective as explaining a joke!

The lesson develops successfully only if the learners can be persuaded to accept responsibility for 'sorting out the mess' – making sense of the situation to their own and one another's satisfaction. If they are watching and waiting to see when the teacher is satisfied with their answers, the dynamics are wrong. Sense-imposing is a natural human tendency (small children live like this all the time), so learners should be able to become comfortable operating in this way. Teachers are also natural order-imposers so, if the learners are to gain anything, the teacher will have to learn to feel comfortable holding back and will have to resist falling into 'explaining mode'.

Therefore, the teacher

◆ avoids suggesting or encouraging any particular approach to resolution;

◆ encourages clear communication about the thinking;

◆ perhaps highlights difficulties with the learners' ideas as they are presented – almost a 'devil's advocate' – and invites others to respond to whatever is said.

Learners need to feel that it is OK to have a go, try out ideas, get things wrong, take their time and share thoughts with one another.

Lessons in this mould can be a lot of fun. The teacher needs to be prepared for a degree of unpredictability. It may be the learners who are initially surprised with what the teacher offers at the start of the lesson, but the feeling of surprise may shift to the *teacher* as the lesson progresses and the learners come up with novel ideas of resolution.

Example 1.1 **Gradient**

When planning to work on gradient with a Year 8 class, you might choose not to advertise your intentions but instead begin with the following diagram and notions of area:

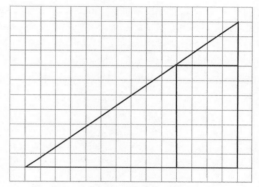

Ask learners to find the areas of each of the two triangles and of the rectangle, reassuring those who complain that this is too easy that everything will be all right (or, rather, *not* all right!) in a minute. Learners might or might not need prompting also to find the area of the entire figure.

The problem they will find is that 'they don't add up': area of large triangle + area of rectangle + area of small triangle ≠ area of whole figure

$$\frac{10 \times 7}{2} + 4 \times 7 + \frac{4 \times 3}{2} \neq \frac{14 \times 10}{2}$$

The two triangles plus the rectangle add up to 69 cm², whereas the entire figure appears to be 70 cm². Unless the learners have seen it before, this should be surprising.

Possible prompts to use with learners would be:

◆ Try to sort out what's going on here.

◆ If you already think you know what's going on, don't tell anyone, but make up one of your own.

◆ If you're completely stuck, try making a *very accurate* copy of the drawing on paper (or perhaps on computer, possibly using *Logo*).

The main thing for the teacher to do is hold back, listen and watch. Giving hints speeds up the lesson but plucks away the opportunities for the learners to engage with the problem for themselves. There is more going on here than eventually encountering ideas connected with gradient. Learners are operating in mathematical ways to resolve difficulties and developing mathematical resourcefulness and resilience.

Typically, perhaps after many ideas have surfaced, a sense emerges that the *slants* of the hypotenuses of the two triangles are not the same; that '10 along and 7 up *isn't the same as* 4 along and 3 up, which *isn't the same as* 14 along and 10 up'. Probing what is meant by 'the same as' in this context leads to words such as 'angle', 'slope' and 'steepness', and a concept of gradient can emerge naturally and be formalised if desired.

Example 1.2 **Area scale factor**

You could begin with a Year 9 or 10 class in this way:

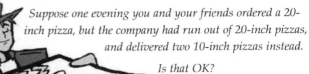

Suppose one evening you and your friends ordered a 20-inch pizza, but the company had run out of 20-inch pizzas, and delivered two 10-inch pizzas instead.

Is that OK?

Many learners will think that this is more or less OK. It is not unusual for the class to be unanimous about this. If there is a lone sceptical voice (possibly the teacher's), it may be hard for them to gain a hearing until they draw a diagram such as this:

At some point after staring at this diagram, it is as though a bomb goes off! There are usually expressions of disbelief ("No Way!") and possibly the checking of '2 × 10 = 20' on calculators!

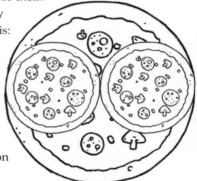

It is clear that the pizza company is cheating here, but how bad is the con?

◆ How much pizza is missing? Why?

◆ How many 10-inch pizzas would you demand to make up for a '20-inch'? Why?

Constructing a diagram with square pizzas can help here, as can diagrams such as this:

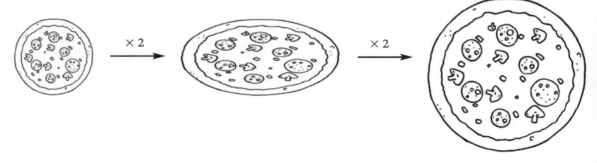

Further avenues might include:

❯ Consideration of how much crust/edge you get in each case.

❯ What if pizzas were described by the length of perimeter/circumference rather than by means of diameter? Would two '10-inches' amount to a '20-inch' then?

Example 1.3 **Dimensions and equations**

Don't flag up in advance that this is going to be 'all about dimensions'; simply begin by offering learners a 'proof' such as the following. (At each stage, the same operation is applied to both sides of the equation.)

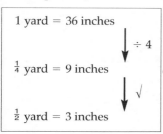

$$1 \text{ yard} = 36 \text{ inches}$$
$$\downarrow \div 4$$
$$\tfrac{1}{4} \text{ yard} = 9 \text{ inches}$$
$$\downarrow \sqrt{}$$
$$\tfrac{1}{2} \text{ yard} = 3 \text{ inches}$$

> Square-rooting both sides seems to make the measurement bigger *and* smaller at the same time!

There is usually some 'shock' with demonstrations such as these. Using a similar approach, learners can 'show' that £1 = 10 pence (by square-rooting £1 = 100 p). The idea that the yards, inches, pounds and pence units are all getting square-rooted, as well as the number of them, is a hard thing to feel comfortable with, and sheds light on why 100 cm^2 is not equal to 1 m^2. This can be a good way of getting into dimensions. What's important is that learners play around until they sense what works and what doesn't.

Other 'dubious proofs' can expose false assumptions and misconceptions in the area of equations, and the following may be worth spending some time worrying about.

'Proof' that 1 = 2

Let $a = b$
Therefore, $\quad a^2 = ab$
So $\qquad a^2 - b^2 = ab - b^2$
$$(a - b)(a + b) = b(a - b)$$
$$a + b = b$$
$$b + b = b$$
$$2b = b$$
$$2 = 1$$

'Proof' that a dog has nine legs!

No dog has five legs (obviously).
One dog has four legs.
Let's do this in algebra: $\quad 0d = 5$
$$1d = 4$$
Adding the equations gives $\quad 1d = 9$
So one dog has nine legs!

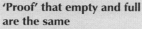

'Proof' that empty and full are the same

$$\tfrac{1}{2} \text{ full} = \tfrac{1}{2} \text{ empty}$$
$$\downarrow \times 2$$
$$\text{full} = \text{empty}$$

'Proof' that school dinners are better than heaven!

A school dinner is better than nothing. (But is it?)
Nothing is better than heaven.
Therefore a school dinner is better than heaven:

school dinner > nothing > heaven

Clearly, it isn't sufficient merely to disbelieve the conclusion for any of these proofs. The whole point is *Why is it false?* Does it start out wrongly? If not, *where* does it go wrong? Trying to fox others with learners' own creations can be fun. The desperation experienced when facing these is testimony to the conviction that mathematics *must* fit together and not contain contradictions such as these, that would bring down the whole system.

There are links here to the history of mathematics and how ideas have come to be accepted. Keen learners might be interested in finding out something about the work of Kurt Gödel.

2 It must be one or the other

The sense that two mutually contradictory things cannot both be true simultaneously goes very deep in human beings. So a situation in which there is the potential to see things in two clashing ways can be useful in developing understanding, especially if some learners take one view and others the opposite. The necessity to choose one way or the other can push thinking forward. A tactile or sensory 'feel' to the context can also be helpful, rooting the discussion in 'reality'.

Example 2.1 **Ratio**

A good setting for talking about ratio is one in which the thing that is the same when the 'ratio' is the same is easily *felt*. Taste is a natural possibility, especially if both of the components of the mixture have some easily describable quality (i.e., neither is water).

Suppose you mix 10 litres of orange juice and 4 litres of lemonade. That makes 14 litres of fizzy orange. Another time there are more people, so you mix 11 litres of orange juice with 5 litres of lemonade, to make 16 litres altogether.

Will the drinks taste the same or different? Why?

Taste is sufficiently 'grounded' for learners to feel that it must be either the same or different – it is unusual for a young person not to have an opinion on this. If different, will it taste more 'orangey' or more 'fizzy'? Discussion normally makes reference to other possible mixtures, so a table such as the one below can be an aid to discussion, filling in the quantities as various possibilities are considered.

	A	B				
orange	10	11				
lemonade	4	5				

Thrashing out different ideas can cement why the concept of ratio is a helpful way of looking at a situation such as this. Answers involving the word 'ratio' tend not to help!

Follow-up questions might include:

◆ *Which ones will taste the same as this one? Why?*

◆ *Which ones will taste more 'orangey' and which ones will taste more 'lemonadey'?*

Paint is another obvious context (and red and white may be easier colours to talk about than, say, blue and white, because of the availability of the words 'pink' and 'pinki-ness'). However, the more vivid sensory aspect of taste seems to make for a more powerful generator of opinions than the perhaps vaguer visual impression of colour.

Example 2.2 **Percentages**

There are plenty of easy ways to start an argument here. For example:

Is a 10% increase followed by a 20% decrease the same as a 20% decrease followed by a 10% increase. If not, is it more or less?

How does a 10% increase followed by a 10% increase compare with a 20% increase?

What on earth would you do?

 This type of lesson is based on an appeal to basic human resourcefulness. Set up a contrived situation and ask learners what they would do. Some sense that the stakes might be high can be helpful. A no-rules-anything-goes approach allows questioning of the terms of the problem, and intrinsic creativity can lead to a lot of productive thinking.

Example 3.1 **Constructions**

Why use compass-and-straight-edge constructions to make a right angle when the same box you carry your compasses in probably also contains a protractor – an easier and more accurate instrument to use? Here is an idea that could lead to some work on constructions:

Imagine you were shipwrecked onto an uninhabited island. You keep up one another's spirits by holding out hope of a rescue for as long as you can. Eventually, though, you begin to face the possibility of being stranded here for the rest of your lives. So you start to build a civilisation, but all your belongings have been lost at sea, and all you have is what you can find on the island. There's wood, and sharp stones to cut with, and plenty of reeds that you can make into rope. But to make sturdy buildings you need a right angle. Once you have something that is right-angled you can copy it, but how do you get the first right angle?

This is certainly not intended as a realistic scenario; more of a challenge to consider how you would manage without some of the things we take for granted in our society.

All sorts of ideas may arise – and it doesn't matter if making circles in the sand (leading to the standard construction) isn't one of them. The properties of a right angle are being considered, and this is a task that can lead to a stronger appreciation of the significance of right angles generally. Ideas involving improvised plumb-lines or folded leaves can be indicative of considerable thought. Even if the teacher is forced to present the standard construction herself, it is likely to be received with far more 'wonder' than might have been the case without the thinking involved in a task such as this.

Related questions might include:

❭ How did they make the first protractor? How did they know where to put the marks? Could you make one on your island? How?

❭ Could you make 'a degree' exactly the same size as the degrees we have in our culture? How? Would it matter?

❭ Could you make a centimetre exactly like ours? A second? A gram? How?

❭ Why can the information necessary for some units be 'carried around in our heads' (i.e., can't be lost in a shipwreck) whereas for other units we need an object to hand?

❭ If you could make up new units systems for measurement, what would you deliberately change and what would you try to keep the same? Why?

Example 3.2 **Probability**

A good way to get some involvement and investment in a problem is to ask learners to decide on a course of action. Something is at stake, even if only in theory. It can be amusing to witness the heated emotions on show, for instance, in an imaginary game involving an absurd and unfair distribution of theoretical sweets!

A simple example concerns the spinner below:

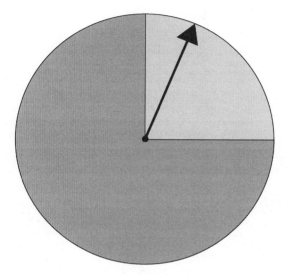

One quarter of the spinner is coloured yellow; three quarters is red. When spun, the spinner is just as likely to stop at any point on the circumference.

Choose a colour – if it stops on your colour, you win.

If you had four goes at this game, which colour would you choose for each of the goes?

Would it depend on what had come up on the previous goes?

Make a rule for what the best strategy is.

Why is it the best strategy?

Games like this can be tried practically (using either real spinners or their ICT equivalent) to see whether choosing red each time is a good idea – even if it's the fourth go and you've already had three reds. The so-called *Gambler's Fallacy* can be very strong!

Devising probability games that are fun to play can be a challenging task. Rigging games so that you are more likely to win than your opponent – but keeping the game close enough for it not to be too obvious – can be difficult. (This is a good thing, I suppose.)

❭ Design a two-player game in which there is an advantage in either going first or going second.

'I will tell you the rules for my game, and you will then have 30 seconds to think about it and decide whether you want to go first or second. Then we will play it and see who wins!'

❭ Are you more likely to get a six with one fair die or a *total* of six when throwing *two* fair dice? Given the choice, which would you go for?

❭ Find out what the *Monty Hall Problem* is and think about why it provokes so much debate and disagreement.

Paying to Play

1 Design a game of chance in which it is possible to win some money.

2 Would you play this game? How much might you be willing to pay to play this game? Why?

3 How much would you need to charge if you were going let other people play this game and you wanted to make money out of it? Why?

Even simple-sounding games can be very hard to analyse theoretically, but an experimantal relative frequency approach can always be employed.

The sky's the limit

Only the start of this sort of lesson can be anticipated: once you set it going you need to stand well back. Ideas can shoot off in many different directions, like a blaze at a fireworks factory.

This sort of lesson gives scope for learners to develop an idea however they see fit. There should be a creative feel, with perhaps some similarity to composition based on a given theme in music.

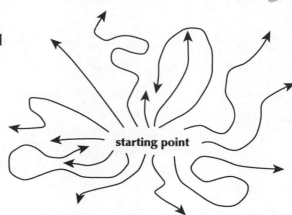

starting point

Differentiation by outcome can be very successful with encouragement and some guidance and planning by the teacher. Pupils take routes and arrive at destinations that work well for them at that moment and extend their understanding from where they are. The teacher's preparation consists of considering what she might expect from different learners, coupled with a determination not to be limited by those expectations once the lesson begins.

Issues to consider might include:

◆ being willing to work with learners on lines of enquiry that the teacher did not anticipate

◆ how to share different learners' achievements in a way that doesn't make anyone feel small or lose face: the 'p's – plenary, poster, presentation, photograph?

◆ how to encourage a learner with an overly ambitious aim perhaps to start with something simpler and build up to the bigger plan later, without communicating a low view of their capability

◆ how to encourage a learner who seems to aim low to try something more complex, supporting them as they do so

◆ anticipating problems/needs as much as possible, and making sure that resources are available before they are needed, without constraining options unnecessarily or pushing down a pre-determined route

◆ deciding how and when to stop the activity without discouraging the 95% who 'haven't finished yet'. It might be helpful to encourage a view, as with Art, that *tasks like these are never finished; they just stop in interesting places.*

Sometimes it may be helpful to consider the 'level' of the work produced; e.g., 'Make up an easy / medium / hard example' or 'Tell us your most impressive idea / the one you're most proud of / something you think it's unlikely anyone else has thought of'. At other times it may be very hard to decide what the 'standard' of a particular piece of work might be.

Example 4.1 **Volume and density**

A simple starting point can lead to some challenging and interesting work.

Design some gold coins that are worth various amounts of money; say, £10, £100 or £1000.

Be accurate about any measurements you state.

Learners will need to know values such as the density of gold (19.32 g/cm^3) and its price (varying by the minute, but around £10 per gram on the markets at the time of writing).

Areas likely to be encountered include:

◆ conversions among currencies, mass, density, volume, lengths

◆ similarity, if the coins of different value are going to be enlargements of each other

◆ calculation of the volume of cuboids, cylinders, prisms and other more exotic shapes

◆ rounding and errors, since gold is valuable!

Example 4.2 **Design a game**

If pupils are always asking "Can we play a game today?", a surprise response might be, "Yes, if you make one." There is often far more mathematical activity in creating a game than there is in playing a commercially-produced one.

The notion of a 'game' often tends to be interpreted as 'board game' or 'card game'; and the focus goes on making the materials. However, many excellent games involve no 'stuff' at all and this may be worth pointing out. The class can be divided into groups to prepare the games, and a deadline set, at which point (whatever state the game is in) games are rotated, and each group plays another group's game. Sometimes feedback is given. You could try insisting that pupils write detailed, unambiguous, short, easy-to-follow instructions so that others can work out what to do. This often turns out to be the most difficult aspect of the whole exercise, although a valuable one. There may be opportunities here for cross-curricular work with the English department. Another model is for 'creators' to move round with their game, teaching it to the other groups. Often there are unforeseen eventualities, rules need to be created and disagreements resolved on the hoof, but this generally involves a need for clear thinking and so can be a very worthwhile element of the process.

When each group has played each game, the games can be evaluated:

- *Is this game fun to play? Why / why not?*
- *Would you want to play it more than once? Why / why not?*
- *How could you adapt / improve the game?*
- *What do you need to know about maths to play this game?*
- *What do you learn by playing it?*

Example 4.3 **Graphs**

It may not sound like it, but using computer software to draw pictures can be a highly mathematical activity. Pupils may feel that they are messing about, but none of the following tasks can be accomplished well without a significant amount of detailed mathematical reasoning.

Logo

- Use commands like **fd** and **lt** and so on to draw a house / block of flats.
- Add some windows (make a procedure for a window?) and a door.
- Draw a road outside with a dashed white line (**repeat** command?) . . . and so on.

Graph-Plotting Package (e.g., Omnigraph or Autograph)

- Try entering $y = \sqrt{x^2} \pm \sqrt{1-x^2}$, and be surprised by the picture!
- See what other pictures you can make: people, animals, aliens, people's initials?

A lot of the maths happens when you get close to something you like and want to modify it. What is the effect of replacing all the xs with $2x$? Or putting '+1' on the end?, etc. Sometimes surprises prompt mathematical questions; e.g., 'Why is $x^{100} + y^2 = 1$ a pretty good square?' (Such shapes are sometimes called 'supercircles' or 'squircles'.)

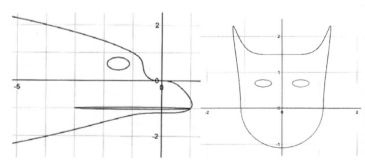

So the classic Art cover lesson ('Draw a picture of the person sitting next to you') can now be a maths lesson too!

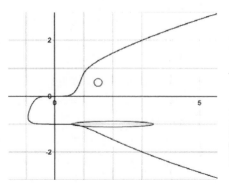

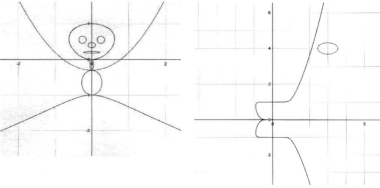

Plunging into deep waters

 This is 'cavernous maths' – a low entry but a high ceiling. In other words, it is easy to make a start and get into the problem, but to achieve anything like a 'complete' solution will really take some doing.

A lot of mathematics questions are easy to answer when you understand what is being asked – the question is complicated but the answer is simple. The main difficulty is interpreting the question, making sense of the notation, the language, the diagram, etc. Quite a lot of secondary school algebra can be answered by small children if the question is explained in terms they are familiar with. The kind of lesson described here is the opposite and involves a question that may be simple to state but very difficult to answer. Everyone can understand the problem; the hard bit is answering it. This is surely the way it should be.

Some suggestions for beginning these lessons might be:

◆ Consider being explicit about the level of challenge that you anticipate – perhaps by indicating how long you plan to spend on this task.

◆ Don't be fazed by learners who panic or say they will never be able to do it or claim that it is impossible to do anything - all we have to worry about initially is starting; once you get going it is easier to move on.

◆ Distinuish questions 'of clarification' from other kinds of question, perhaps allowing the former but not the latter? "It may seem hard, but does the task make sense?"

◆ If necessary, encourage learners to simplify the problem initially (specialise, make arbitrary decisions, impose constraints) in order to get going and gain a feel for the situation. Later on, encourage the opposite (generalising, extending and making the problem more complex) so that there is a sense of building up towards solving the whole thing.

◆ Different members of a small group might work on different aspects or instances of the problem and then compare their results.

Puzzle books are full of suitable tasks, such as the following:

Example 5.1 **Camel crossing**

A camel has to carry 3 000 bananas across a 1 000 mile desert. There are two conditions:

1   *The camel can carry only 1 000 bananas at a time.*

2   *The camel eats one banana for each mile he travels.*

What is the maximum number of bananas that can reach the other side of the desert? How do you know this is the best answer?

Diagrams/graphs that can helpfully represent this problem are many and varied. There is a lot of potential for different approaches and possible cases to be analysed. The large numbers may encourage the trying of cases involving smaller numbers, perhaps using plastic cubes to represent bananas. A spreadsheet might help with some of the number crunching.

Example 5.2 **Dominoes**

◆ *How many spots are there altogether on a normal set of dominoes?*
How can you convince others that your answer is right?

◆ *Imagine a set of dominoes that goes from 0-0 up to 10-10. How many spots altogether would there be on that set?*

◆ *Or on a set that goes up to 100-100?*

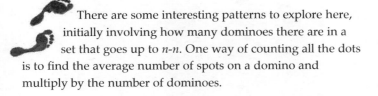

There are some interesting patterns to explore here, initially involving how many dominoes there are in a set that goes up to *n-n*. One way of counting all the dots is to find the average number of spots on a domino and multiply by the number of dominoes.

Example 5.3 **Cyclic numbers**

Find this 5-digit number:

        ✱   ✱   ✱

With a '1' after it, it is three times as large as it is with a '1' before it.

Make up some problems like this.

This can seem impossible at first but a bit of logic (or algebra) will pay off.

Example 5.4 **Palindromic numbers**

These are numbers like 5273725, which are the same when read forwards or backwards. Palindromes are words like 'racecar', which have the same property.

5273725

How many 7-digit palindromic numbers are there? Why?

How many palindromic numbers are there of other lengths?

The patterns in the answers may be surprising but can be explained without needing algebra.

Example 5.5 **Alphametics**

These are puzzles in which each letter stands for one digit. Good ones require a lot of logical and careful thinking to solve. It is often the case that if you make up ones involving pupils' own names they are much more enthusiastic about solving them than if they say things like 'SEND + MORE = MONEY'. They look very hard initially, but once you get going and rule out some possibilities or make a decision about a letter or two it gets much easier.

```
  RIKESH          STUART
   KATIE           RIARN        TIERAN         GEORGE
+    ANI         + PETER       +  KATE        + PETER
---------        --------      --------       --------
 THEBEST          GENIUS        RULEOK         TROUBLE
```

A lot of incidental arithmetic practice happens without even noticing.

A new angle

 We get used to representing certain things in certain ways. Bringing more variety into how we view mathematical objects can help learners to make connections they have not made before. In the Indian story of the blind men and the elephant, each man touched the elephant to find out what it was like. When they compared notes afterwards, they had completely different ideas about an elephant because they each touched a different part, such as the trunk or an ear. Tasks in which everyone can take a different perspective and contribute something of value seem to be less common in mathematics than they are in other subjects.

Example 6.1 **Fractions**

Close your eyes and imagine 'a half'.

Now open your eyes and draw what you saw.

Doing this individually (mini-white-boards?) or as a whole-class activity can be enlightening and lead to a lot of discussion. The outcomes here show some familiar and less familiar ideas connected with a half, many of which required explanation from the learner who drew them.

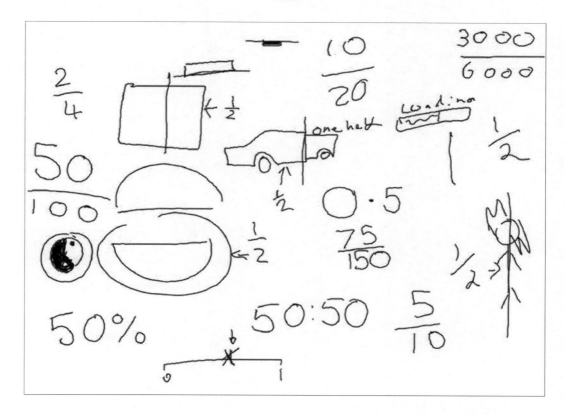

Example 6.2 **Walking graphs**

The saying 'a picture is worth 1000 words' encourages us to illustrate wordy statements to aid clarity and appreciation. But what if the object under consideration is already a picture, such as a graph or a shape? Finding different ways of representing visual images can deepen learners' understanding of related ideas. Playing the *Fourbidden* game (ATM) and being forced to articulate 'rectangle' in words, without waving your arms in the air, pushes thinking into the properties of 'rectangleness'. Another fun one is to describe 'a circle' over the telephone to a friendly alien who doesn't understand when you say 'round' or 'like the sun'. It is often easier to say 'what you do to make one' rather than 'what one is'. Learners can sit in pairs back-to-back and one has to draw what the other describes. Cross-curricular links with English speaking and listening tasks may be possible.

You can experience a graph by walking along its shape on the floor or by physically being one point of it among many others (standing in a line). Attention is focused very differently in these cases, and they contrast with the more usual global appreciation of a static graph on the page.

Set up some axes on the ground in a large open space.
Stand in position to be the graph of $y = x$.
Now keep your x-coordinate the same but double/half/multiply by -3 your y-coordinate.
What graph are you now?
Who moved the furthest/least? Who didn't move?
Who would move most if we changed from
$y = x$ into $y = x^2$? etc

Example 6.3 **Singing graphs**

Learners may be used to experiencing graphs visually as a static image and possibly dynamically as a left-to-right developing line. The impact of these alternatives can be considerably different. Often these pictures are linked to tables of numbers. A different way of experiencing a graph might be as a *sound*, where the pitch relates to the '*y*-value', while the '*x*-value' operates as time.

The program *SoundFunction* is available free at **www.foster77.co.uk/variety/** and enables the user to enter a list of numbers (perhaps pasting in a column of values from a spreadsheet) and the computer generates the accompanying soundtrack. (Zero is taken as middle C and an increase of 1 unit corresponds to a semitone musically.) A collection of ready-made mp3 files is also available, representing familiar functions in an unfamiliar way.

Possible tasks might include:

Predict how particular graphs might sound or try to identify graphs from their sounds.

Which graphs sound 'boring/predictable'? Why?

Which graphs sound 'surprising'? Why?

Which graphs are 'soprano'/'bass' graphs? Why?

Which graphs are in your singing range?

What are the aural effects of transformations such as $f(x) \rightarrow f(x) + a$ and $f(x) \rightarrow af(x)$ and $f(x) \rightarrow -f(x)$, etc?

Example 6.4 **Singing sequences**

It is also possible to use *SoundFunction* to represent sequences.

What do the square numbers 'sound like'?

How would you tell the square numbers from the cube numbers?

How does an arithmetic series sound different from a geometric series?

Do you need perfect (i.e., absolute) pitch to tell one sequence from another?

When is difference in relative pitch sufficient?

Example 6.5 **Simultaneous equations**

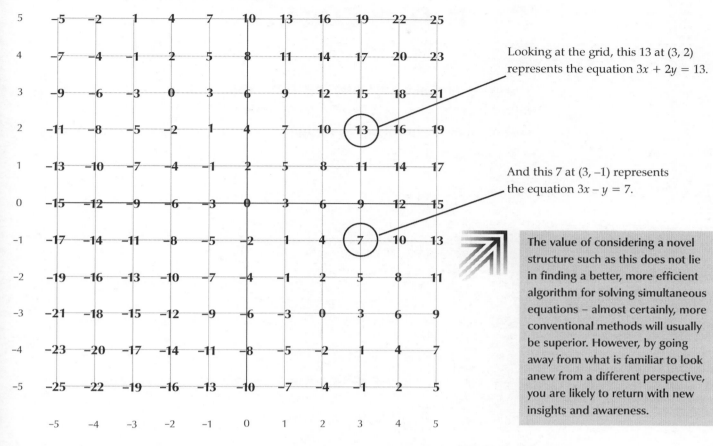

Looking at the grid, this 13 at (3, 2) represents the equation $3x + 2y = 13$.

And this 7 at (3, –1) represents the equation $3x – y = 7$.

> The value of considering a novel structure such as this does not lie in finding a better, more efficient algorithm for solving simultaneous equations – almost certainly, more conventional methods will usually be superior. However, by going away from what is familiar to look anew from a different perspective, you are likely to return with new insights and awareness.

Learners may be familiar with representing the solution of two simultaneous linear equations by the intersecting point of two straight-line graphs. The grid above is a different representation that can lead to some deep thinking about how simultaneous equations work.

Find two more points on the grid and say what equations they represent.

How can you use two grid numbers and their positions to find the values of x and y?

Which sorts of positions of the two values are easiest/hardest to handle? Why?

How do these values of x and y lead to the values on the rest of the grid?

Describe how to produce a grid like this one for another pair of values of x and y.

Are there any pairs of simultaneous equations that cannot be solved by this method?

Are there any kinds of pairs of simultaneous equations that are particularly well-suited to this method?

Do you like this method? Would you use it? When? Why / why not?

Example 6.6 **Polygons**

A deliberate attempt to see familiar 2-D shapes differently might be to see them as projections of 3-D solids:

Which polygons can be the shadow of a cube?
Which polygons can be the shadow of a cuboid?

Learners may be used to seeing shapes as cut-outs from card, but focusing instead on the overlapping area of two or more pieces of card can lead to seeing things afresh:

Which kinds of polygons can be made as the overlapping region of two identical square pieces of card? What if the squares are of different sizes?

Which kinds of polygons can be made as the overlapping region of two equilateral triangle pieces of card? What about using one square and one equilateral triangle?

How do you know that you have found all the possible kinds of shape?

Action – reaction

This feels a bit like a science practical lesson. You do something that might be regarded as a kind of 'corporate experiment', having some sort of shared experience, and then you stop and reflect and discuss what happened.

The starting 'event' might be a *Flash* computer animation, such as one showing a point moving steadily around the circumference of a circle viewed from various vantage points; e.g., 'front-on', side-view and plan-view, providing an insight into the sine and cosine functions. It is not enough simply to have the experience; the discussion about what it might mean is essential.

Example 7.1 **Locus**

This is a topic with lots of possibilities for outdoor or big-open-space-indoor people maths. A less common locus you might do relates to the Circle of Apollonius, though obviously calling it that at the outset would kill the activity!

Anoopa stand there. Ben stand there.

1 *Now, everyone else, stand so that you're **twice** as far from Anoopa as you are from Ben.*

2 *Make some conjectures.*

3 *Now stand so that you're **three times** as far from Anoopa as you are from Ben.*

4 *And so on, with different **multiplying** factors.*

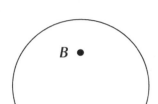

After some initial confusion and once any arguments have subsided, learners should be standing in an approximate circle. But …

♦ Is it really a proper circle or just a curvy kind of shape? How do you know?

♦ And, if it is a circle, how do its features (location of centre and length of radius) relate to where Anoopa and Ben are standing? What happens if they move?

♦ And what happens when the multiplying factor becomes different from 2? Could it be negative?

♦ What happens if the multiplying factor is slightly more or slightly less than 1? What if it is equal to 1 *exactly*?

Graph paper and pencil, graph-plotting software or dynamic geometry software might be appropriate tools for probing what is going on.

Example 7.2 **Multiplication by powers of ten**

Chairs in a line represent place value columns (H, T, U, etc) and learners holding numbers written large on A4 paper represent digits. After multiplying and dividing by ten, a hundred, 0.1 and so on, the discussion can focus on who went where when, from the point of view of the individual digits as well as the general audience.

Then let the *chairs* represent digits and the moving learners carry signs saying H, T, U, etc. Who moves where when now? Why?

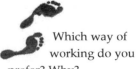

Which way of working do you prefer? Why?

Would you sometimes think one way and sometimes another? When? Why?

Realms of possibility

Teachers can have mixed feelings about offering learners tasks which are impossible. On the one hand, the notion of impossibility, and the ability to say that something *definitely cannot be* is fundamental to mathematics and deeply empowering. In other areas of human endeavour, it is usually the height of arrogance to say that something definitely can't be done, whereas it is a vital part of mathematics. Yet, on the other hand, teachers may not want to discourage and frustrate learners by deceiving them into investing time on something that will be unsuccessful.

Possibility tables offer one way through this, because the idea of possibility and impossibility is 'on the table' from the start. The idea is that you have two varying factors running horizontally and vertically and in each cell you give an example of something that satisfies the column and row headings for that cell, or if you think it is impossible you explain why.

Learners can work in groups on A3 versions of these tables, using pencil, as this seems to encourage discussion in a 'conjecturing atmosphere'.

Note that the cells in these tables would have to be big enough to contain drawings of shapes.

Example 8.2 **Symmetry**

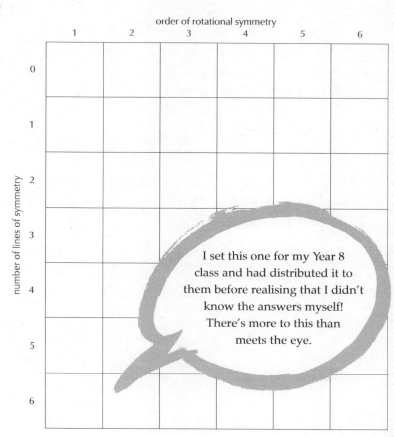

Example 8.1 **Triangles**

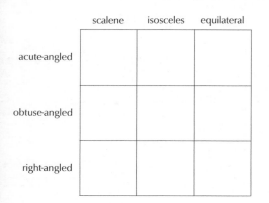

Example 8.3 **Polygons and angles**

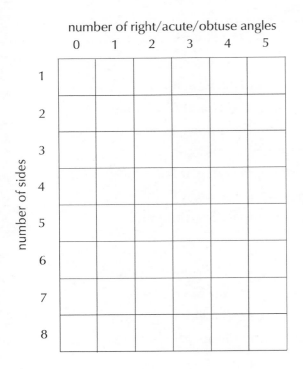

Example 8.4 **Polyominoes**

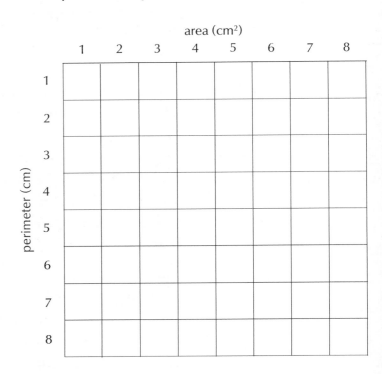

Example 8.5 **Polygons and parallel sides**

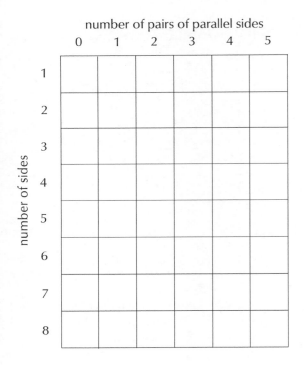

Example 8.6 **3-D Solids**

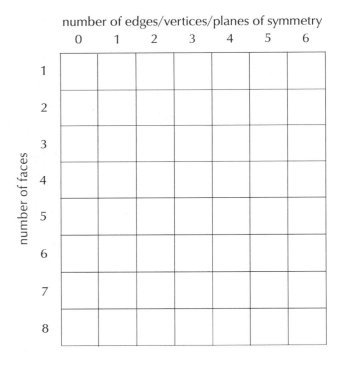

There is a freedom about the orderly nature of the column and row headings; nothing is being concealed – the learner is not being protected from complexity – there are no arbitrary constraints to hide mathematical awkwardness. Everything is available to be inspected and considered.

Just explore!

This can feel like the most natural lesson of all. Simply take a rich idea and see what happens when you play with it. The details of the original problem become unimportant – what matters is finding out as much as you can and following your instincts. There is nothing mysterious about 'doing an investigation'; this is what small children do naturally within their environment – no-one has to tell them that they are supposed to be curious and investigative; they just are. (And human beings perhaps learn faster in their first years doing their own thing than at any time in the future!)

Example 9.1 **Trigonometry**

The following task could be presented to Year 9 or older pupils who have some knowledge of Pythagoras' Theorem and trigonometry in right-angled triangles:

Getting home

A turtle leaves his front door facing North and immediately turns left 10° and walks 10 m.

He then turns right 20° and walks 20 m.

He then turns left 30° and walks 30 m.

How much does he have to turn, and which way, to face back towards his house?

How far must he walk to get back home?

The mentioning of a turtle could encourage a *Logo* approach. A spreadsheet might also aid any number-crunching; a difficult challenge is to produce a spreadsheet (see below) which generates the answer when up to, say, ten lines of fd and lt commands are entered (where lt might be negative).

fd	lt

To get home, the turtle must go
fd _____ m
lt _____ °.

Pencil and paper might be used for accurate drawings or for mathematical sketches to aid calculation.

The numbers chosen in the problem are intended to encourage extending and generalising by the learner:

◆ What can you change about this problem?

◆ How can you make the problem easier to solve?

◆ How can you make the problem harder to solve?

◆ How far can you go purely with your imagination? Can you give an approximate answer without writing anything down?

◆ Could you go into three dimensions; i.e., call on a flying turtle?

Example 9.2 **Iteration**

The following iterative investigation can go on more or less forever (like iteration!), as small changes to the process can make a huge difference to the difficulty of analysis. With an appropriate level of complexity, this can provide food for thought for virtually anyone, whatever mathematics they may already know.

Learners are asked to follow the flow diagram below choosing an operation, or later operations, to put in place of the question mark. A good one to start with is '+ 2'. Even learners with a lot of knowledge of mathematics may be surprised by what happens.

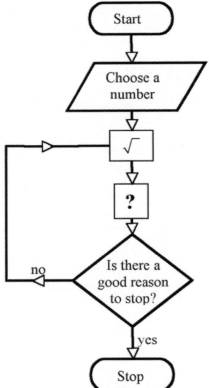

Data can be quickly obtained if the investigation is carried out on a spreadsheet. In the process of investigating, it is likely that graphs will be drawn at some stage, possibly including 'staircase diagrams' such as the one below.

Questions that could be asked include:

◆ Should we keep on iterating for ever or is there a point at which it is sensible to stop? When? Why? Are there *different reasons* why you might decide to stop?

◆ What difference does the starting number make to what happens?
Are there any *impossible* or *awkward* starting numbers?

◆ What difference does the '?' operation make? Try +, −, × and ÷ operations.
What others could you try? You could try more than one operation.

◆ What would you have to choose for '?' to make the sequence converge to $7 / \sqrt{2} / \pi / -1 / 0$?
Which '?' operations lead to convergence to *an integer*?

◆ What diagrams/tables help with making sense of the process?

◆ What would happen if the $\sqrt{}$ operation were changed into something else; for example, $\sqrt[3]{?}$

◆ Can you use algebra to prove your conjectures?

There are possible links with many mathematical ideas; for instance, the golden ratio. The algebra involved in proving the various results by solving equations such as $\sqrt{x} + 2 = x$ can be accessible and interesting to learners who have met quadratic equations.

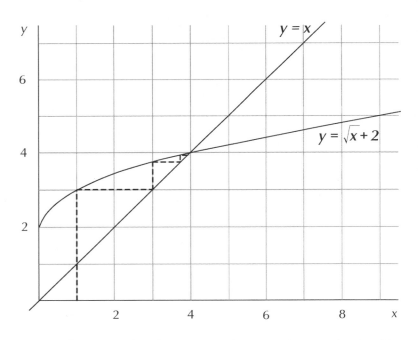

Points of Departure (ATM) are a very rich source of 'Just Explore' problems.

Being the teacher

Being the teacher for a lesson, or even just for a few minutes, can be an attractive proposition for many pupils. Only the teacher can decide how this might be workable with particular classes, but the benefits of working in this way for a lesson or two can extend well beyond those particular episodes – developing a sense that mathematics is far bigger than us and the social conventions that we conform to on a daily basis.

Mathematics is a subject where a much younger and less experienced learner can not only know better than the teacher on a particular occasion but actually prove that they are right, without having to refer to other 'authorities'. The absolute nature of mathematical truth can give learners the sense that they know what they are talking about and are not going to be proved wrong by anyone, no matter how important. It is interesting to see how some pupils suddenly display far greater confidence when 'in role' at the front, in a setting where it is suddenly acceptable to know a lot.

There are many different ways in which pupils might share or take over the role of the teacher. For example, a task for early-finishers in a lesson might be to assume the role of 'experts' and to circulate around the room assisting others. They might be encouraged to try to do so in the sort of way that the teacher might, avoiding telling peers what to do but instead asking them questions about what they are doing. It would be a mistake to think that this is of benefit only to those being assisted.

Example 10.1 **Teaching a younger class**

Year 8 pupils might be invited to plan a mathematics lesson for a Year 7 class. Planning could be carried out in small groups over a series of lessons, the plans 'performed' or explained to the rest of the Year 8 class, and then one or two groups chosen to teach the Year 7 class.

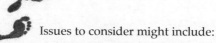

Issues to consider might include:

- Using a topic or investigation that a majority of pupils are reasonably comfortable with; e.g., Year 8 revise directed numbers by teaching what they know to Year 7. If the ideas are new to the 'teaching class', then they will need some opportunity to work on them before they will be ready to plan with Year 7 in mind.

- The extent to which Year 8 are aware of the likely knowledge/interests/etc of Year 7. This could form the basis of plenary discussions.

- The need to cater for different Year 7 learners.

- Appropriate resources (e.g., keeping any photo-copying affordable).

- The possibility of an alternative conclusion to the project for those not chosen to work with the Year 7s; e.g., posting their lesson ideas (e.g., *PowerPoints*) on the school intranet for Year 7 to look at afterwards or making a wall display of ideas.

- The teacher's responsibility for the learning and fair treatment of Year 7 learners as well as the Year 8s.

Example 10.2 **Something completely different…**

Encouraging a pupil to take responsibility for part of a lesson can dramatically improve the dynamics within a class. Choosing the right thing at the right moment is not easy. When Sudokus began to appear in newspapers, a Year 9 learner got hooked on them and wanted to tell the rest of the class about them. At that time no-one else in the class had even heard of them. The Year 9 pupil planned a lesson that involved explaining the rules and providing 'easy' and 'hard' puzzles, and the class worked far more enthusiastically and intensely on her tasks than they would have done if the idea had been presented by the teacher.

Issues to consider might include:

◆ Allowing the pupil to *begin* the lesson and go on as long as feels right; the teacher being ready to take over with something else when necessary. This is more comfortable than trying to rush the pupil's slot into 10 minutes at the end.

◆ Making other pupils aware that they may get 'their turn' in the future can encourage a more supportive and less challenging atmosphere, especially if the new 'teacher' appears nervous.

◆ Encouraging constructive comments from the class afterwards may or may not be helpful, depending on the classroom culture.

Sometimes pupils constantly pester their maths teacher with logical puzzles or conundrums or riddles. Some pupils who have learned mathematical magic tricks want an audience. These can form the basis for memorable lessons, perhaps towards the end of term.

Example 10.3 **Research presentations**

This probably happens more often in other subjects than in mathematics, although why should this be the case? The idea is to book a computer room or library for several lessons and pupils, perhaps in groups, are given some choice over what they research. Each group then presents their findings to the rest of the class. An enthusiastic Year 8 class once ran this like an academic 'colloquium', introducing the speakers formally, chairing questions, booking the school lecture theatre and inviting other members of staff.

Presentations could be on any area of mathematics, and this can be one way of approaching the history of mathematics without boring pupils by lecturing at them.

Possible topics for presentations might include:

◆ A mathematician, or a couple of contemporaries; e.g., Euclid, Archimedes, Erdos, Fibonacci, Euler, Pythagoras, Pascal, Galois, Gauss, Einstein, Leibniz, Gödel, von Neumann, Mandelbrot, Ramanujan, Laplace, Lagrange, Riemann, Wiles, Escher, Diophantus, Möbius (see www.dcs.warwick.ac.uk/bshm/resources.html#indiv).

◆ Women mathematicians (www.scottlan.edu./lriddle/women/women.htm).

◆ Maths in sport / computers / music / code-breaking / weather-forecasting / science and engineering / art / gambling / religion / during a particular historical period or in a particular culture or part of the world.

No teacher is likely to know all of this material, but some awareness of suitable books and websites will be necessary in order to avoid chaos and frustration.

Example 10.4 **Teacher as pupil**

The teacher can work in front of pupils 'in role', stating that she is going to make deliberate mistakes 'live'. It is the pupils' job to correct them and offer advice, either as they happen or afterwards, possibly after some opportunity for discussion in groups.

Example 10.5 **Marking work**

It is common in mathematics classrooms for learners to mark their own or each other's work, often just ticking and crossing. However, developing a culture in which constructive detailed peer feedback is sought, provided and valued can be a big step. It can be easier to begin with imaginary pupils' work; e.g. work from a previous school, or from several years before, which is anonymous. As the teacher, it is worth being on the lookout when marking for mistakes – or particularly good work – containing aspects that are worth discussing and learning from.

For example, the pupil's work below contains several interesting errors:

How do you think the question-writer expected pupils to answer the question? Why?

Why might the pupil have chosen to proceed in this way?

What is good about their answer?

What positive evidence is there here about this pupil's strengths?

What errors can you find? Can you suggest why they may have occurred?

What supportive advice would you give to this learner?

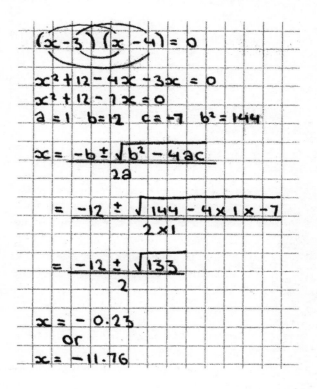

Similar questions might be applied to the piece of work below. (Internal tests – sadly! – provide plenty of material for this kind of activity.)

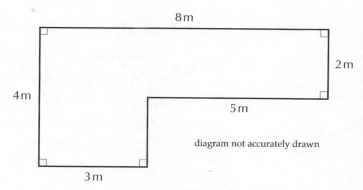

diagram not accurately drawn

The diagram represents an L-shaped room whose corners are all right angles.

(a) Work out the area of the room.

$$(4 \times 8) + (2 \times 5)$$

.......**42**.......m²

(3)

More positively, there are occasions, such as the one below, when there is something to gain from sharing an interesting correct answer:

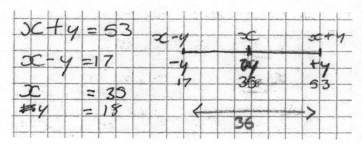

How would you have solved these simultaneous equations?

Can you deconstruct what this pupil did?

Make up a similar problem and solve it her way.

What do you think of her approach? Why?

Stimulus – response

This sort of lesson crystallises out of some initial object of inspiration. It could be a picture, such as a curve-stitching pattern or a 'curve of pursuit' like those shown. There are many beautiful images of such things on the internet as well as some more mundane, though still intriguing, examples.

Example 11.1 **Curve-stitching and curves of pursuit**

Questions that might occur include:

1. What do you see? Straight lines or curves? 2-D or 3-D?

2. What symmetry does the image have?

3. How do you think it was made?

4. Could you make one? What equipment would you need to do it by hand? What software would help? Have a go.

5. What mathematical ideas are buried in it? Do the curves consist of circular arcs?

6. What can you change to make new images?

7. What other questions can you ask?

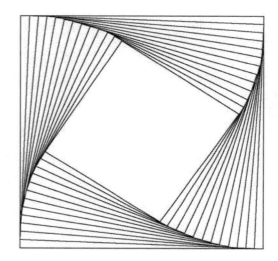

Example 11.2 **Anamorphic art**

Often the first impulse on seeing designs such as these is the simple desire to reproduce the given pattern. This is not necessarily a waste of time. While this is going on, in addition to practising accurate drawing using geometrical instruments, discussion can take place regarding the mathematical properties of the construction.

Go to http://users.skynet.be/J.Beever/pave.htm to see more photographs of Julian Beever's amazing anamorphic pavement drawings. What mathematics do they contain? What questions can you ask?

Example 11.3 **Tessellations**

There is a great deal of beautiful and inspiring mathematical artwork by Maurits Cornelis Escher (1898-1972) at **www.mcescher.com**. Books and posters for the classroom are widely available and can provoke a great deal of thought and reflection.

Dominic

Holly

- ◆ What is the same about both of these tessellating patterns? What is different?
- ◆ What is the same about the repeating units in both patterns? What is different?
- ◆ How do you think these patterns were made?
- ◆ Could you make some designs like these? How?
- ◆ Could you make some tessellating designs where some, or all, of the lines are curves? How?

Example 11.4 **Snowflakes**

- ◆ What occurs to you when you look at these drawings?
- ◆ How do you think they were made? Why?
- ◆ What could you change without destroying the idea? What would stay the same?
- ◆ Could you reproduce them? Could you improve them? How?

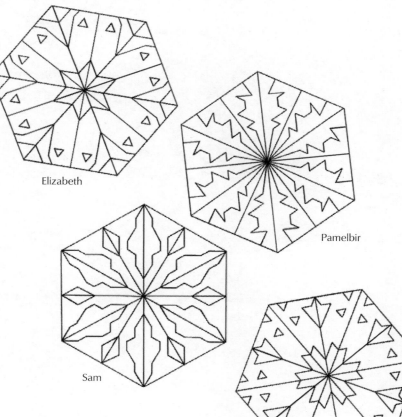

Elizabeth

Pamelbir

Sam

George

Designs such as these can be produced either by paper folding and cutting or by drawing, most easily on isometric paper as here.

Example 11.5 **Footprint**

This is an old classic, which has variations:

We found some rather unusual footprints on the school field early this morning.

(The image would be enlarged to fill an A3 piece of paper.)

As you can see, they're rather large.

Someone said they saw 'a giant man' – that's all we know.

What conjectures can you make about the creature that produced them? Height, weight, walking / running speed, amount of food eaten in a day, depth of impression in damp soil, etc.

What evidence is there that this could be a hoax?

This can be a good opportunity to work on scaling up, with length/area/volume scale factors. The one artefact is enough to produce a lot of analysis.

'Crop circles' may provide another starting point for consideration of scale and perspective – as well as the topic of constructions, if you consider them to be of human origin!

Subsequent related lines of thought might include:

> If you climbed inside a 'doubling machine' that made all distances twice as big (not just perceptually but physically), how would you feel when you got out? Would walking feel the same or different? Why? Would you feel hotter or colder? Would you be stronger? Why?

> If the whole universe and everything in it 'doubled' (all distances) while you were asleep tonight, would you be able to tell in the morning? Why / why not?

> There are applications to biology, such as the effect on different animals of falling a certain height or the relative thickness of different animals' legs.

> There are obvious links with fiction in books such as *Gulliver's Travels* (Swift, 1726), *Alice's Adventures in Wonderland* (Carroll, 1865) and in films including *The Incredible Shrinking Man* (1957), *Fantastic Voyage* (1966) and *Honey, I Shrunk The Kids* (1989).

The great search

This type of lesson exploits 'exhaustive thinking', in which you are not satisfied merely with finding lots of instances of something – the whole point is to *find them all*. Situations requiring exhaustion or systematic consideration of all cases are common in mathematics, and there is a sense of power about knowing that there *cannot possibly* be anything you haven't thought of. Sending learners on a great search to find 'how many ways' can be a particularly interesting kind of lesson, and there are many possible appropriate tasks for this; e.g., geoboard tasks – see Mike Ollerton's books in the bibliography on page 35.

Example 12.1
Words in a maze

Problems like these are commonly found in magazines. Using a word, like MATHS, which has stems which are also real words (ma, mat, math) encourages learners to start with simpler problems and look for structure that will enable them to 'count them all without actually counting them all'. Words which remain real words after repeated curtailment (removal of the final letter) include 'maximals' and 'tamarinds', although some of the words encountered *en route* are a bit obscure. A shorter one, but containing familiar words, is 'erasers'.

Moving from letter to letter, in how many ways can you spell MATHS?

```
              S
          S   H   S
      S   H   T   H   S
    S   H   T   A   T   H   S
S   H   T   A   M   A   T   H   S
    S   H   T   A   T   H   S
      S   H   T   H   S
          S   H   S
              S
```

Helpful questions might include:

◆ How do you know when you've got them all?

◆ How do you know you didn't miss some/one of them?

◆ If someone said they'd got one you hadn't got, what would you say?

◆ Can you see how many there are without counting them all or even imagining them all?

◆ Are there any shortcuts you can find? How do you know they are valid?

 Some ingenuity is necessary to set up similar problems on *isometric* grids.

Example 12.2
Letters in numbers

If you write down the names of the numbers from 1 to 100 (inclusive), how many letters will you write altogether?

Careful systematic thinking is necessary in order to get the same answer twice with this type of problem.

Example 12.3 **Handshakes extended**

The 'handshake problem' is well known:

If everyone in the room shakes hands with everyone else in the room, how many handshakes will there be?

How can you convince everyone that your answer is right?

This can be a nice way to meet triangle numbers or to work on visual representations of a problem. There is a lot of mathematics that can come out of this even if the idea has been used before.

But why stop at 2-people handshakes? The picture on the right illustrates a '3-shake'. When performing a normal '2-shake', most people shake 'twice', for some reason, so younger learners have been known to develop a 'three shakes 3-shake' when performing this greeting.

If everyone 3-shakes with everyone else, how many 3-shakes will there be?

What about 4-shakes?

What about 17-shakes?

If there were 267 people, how many 43-shakes would there be? Why? And so on.

The picture suggests that a 3-shake need not necessarily involve right hands only. This can lead to some extensions:

What difference does it make if *every group* of three people has to 3-shake in *every possible way* (left and right hands)?

What if every possible arrangement of people (*A*, *B* and *C* in the 3-shakes below) counts as different; ie, if these two possibilities are not counted as the same?

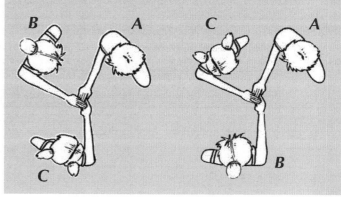

All of these extensions lead to additional opportunities to count or to imagine counting or to discover, for example, that some kind of multiplication is quicker than addition or that powers are quicker than multiplication. They can also generate more insight.

It works – but why?

Mathematical magic tricks are fun and lead naturally to the question 'How does it work?' They can be a good way to encourage learners to ask 'Why?' questions. If you can make things seem like 'tricks', it can sometimes be easier to draw learners into thinking about them.

Example 13.1 **Numerical tricks**

It is easy to find books and websites full of the kind of tricks where you 'magically' end up with 'the number you first thought of'. There are always interesting mathematical ideas inside them; often divisibility properties, such as the digit sum of a multiple of 9 being a multiple of 9.

Elephant maths

1. *Choose an integer between 1 and 9.*
2. *Subtract 5.*
3. *Multiply by 3.*
4. *Square it.*
5. *Add 9.*
6. *Add the digits together.*
7. *Subtract 4.*
8. *Multiply by 2.*
9. *Subtract 6.*
10. *Find the letter of the alphabet corresponding to your number (A=1, B=2, C=3, etc).*
11. *Choose a country that begins with that letter.*
12. *Choose an animal whose name begins with the second letter of the name of the country.*
13. *Think of the colour of that animal …*

… You were thinking of … a … grey … elephant … in … Denmark!

Cards that can spell

Preparation: Lay out a suit of 13 playing cards face down in the following order:

(top) 3 – 8 – 7 – Ace – Queen – 6 – 4 – 2 – Jack – King – 10 – 9 – 5 (bottom)

To begin the trick, hold the stack of cards face down in your hands and count three cards off the top, saying 'A-C-E', placing each, separately, still face down, on the bottom of the pack. Turn over the next card on the top – it is an Ace! Put it to one side. Continue, spelling 'T-W-O', 'T-H-R-E-E' and so on, and each time the next card is the correct one (hopefully!).

After taking your bows, ask learners to discuss how they think it was done – push beyond, "I think he'd put them in a special order at the start" to the specifics. It is a matter of judgment how soon to let learners have cards to play with (one quarter of a pack per group is all that is needed) – perhaps they should try to be sure they have the right order first? One approach is to write down 13 blank spaces and count as you fill in card names in the order Ace – 1 – 2, etc. Another approach is to avoid writing anything down and instead 'reverse engineer' by beginning with the King card and then the Queen and doing the whole process backwards. This is difficult but Year 7s have been able to do it perfectly correctly.

Possible extensions are to adapt the trick so that the cards spell in the opposite order (King first) or so that Ace counts as 'high' or to add in a joker at the end, which of course changes everything. An amusing variation is for each spelling out to fail but instead produce the next card – eg, 'ACE' spells '2' etc.

Example 13.2 **Finger times tables**

It is perhaps surprising that this method is not more widely known. To make use of it, you need to know your tables up to 5 × 5, but those are the easier ones. Then, with practice, you can use your fingers to work out all the rest very quickly and easily.

◆ *To start, you number on each hand from your thumbs 6, 7, 8, 9, 10:*

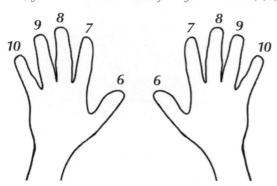

◆ *Suppose you want to work out 7 × 8:*

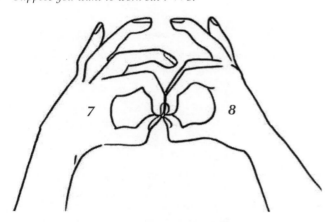

◆ *Make 'seven' with one hand (the left one in the diagram) by putting thumb and first finger together (6 and 7).*

◆ *Make 'eight' with the other hand (the right one in the diagram) by putting thumb, first finger and second finger together (6, 7 and 8).*

In other words, you always use the thumb and also every finger up to and including the one with the number you want for your product.

◆ *To read off the answer, count how many thumbs/fingers are touching: 2 + 3 = 5, and that's the tens digit of the answer. Then look at how many fingers are 'loose' on each hand, and multiply these: 3 × 2 = 6, and that's the units digit of the answer. So 7 × 8 = 56.*

To take another example, for 8 × 8, the thumb and first two fingers of both hands would touch (3 + 3 = 6), leaving two free fingers on each hand (2 × 2 = 4). Hence, 64.

This is often greeted with amazement, sometimes even by mathematics teachers.

 Questions that might be asked include:

◆ Does this always work? How do you know?

◆ How many times tables altogether can you do like this?

◆ Are there any awkward examples / exceptions for this method?

◆ Are you going to incorporate this into your personal 'toolbox'? Why / why not?

It is possible to prove the reliability of this method by exhaustion, since there are only fifteen products to check – this may be a worthwhile exercise for learners. An algebraic proof such as showing that $10(x-5+y-5)+(10-x)(10-y) = xy$ may also be accessible to some learners. The 6 times table, and to a lesser extent, 10 times table 'special cases' can be interesting.

Invent your own maths

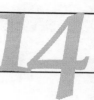

This may not sound like a very good idea, but give it a chance! Being your own boss and rebelling against convention is a big part of being a young person. Sometimes others know better, and learners may discover that mathematically by pursuing the consequences of doing things their way. At other times, their ideas may contain something valuable, at least for themselves and possibly for others too. Being creative with mathematical ideas encourages learners to see mathematics as a 'human' subject rather than a set of absolute principles delivered from outer space!

Example 14.1 **Types of number**

What kinds of numbers are there?

Learners may answer: odd, even, prime, square, triangle, Fibonacci, palindromic,… They are often influenced by the mathematics they have recently been working with and the posters that are on the classroom wall.

What else could we have? Be imaginative with something you know about and try to push it further. Think 'outside the box'.

When you get an idea, see what you can do with it.

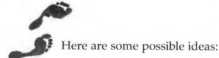

Here are some possible ideas:

◆ We have odd numbers – what about *very odd* numbers? The 'odd odd numbers' 1, 5, 11, etc (every other odd number) are *doubly*-odd. Which numbers are *triply*-odd? How *odd* can a number get? Is there an *oddest* number? What would it be?

◆ We have square numbers – what about *round* numbers? This could refer to their shape (like zero or eight) or 'round numbers' might be 'ball-park figures' like 100 or 1000. Or maybe numbers that make a circle in dots (like the definition of square numbers). How many dots do you need to get a circle?

◆ What about *rectangle* numbers? Would you count 'one-by-something' rectangles? (If so, there would be rather a lot of them!)

◆ How about *trapezium* numbers, *kite* numbers, *rhombus* numbers, *parallelogram* numbers, *arrowhead* numbers, *hexagon* numbers – which of these make any sense at all? Which might be useful or have interesting properties?

◆ Could we define different *sorts* of triangle numbers? *Isosceles-triangle* numbers or *scalene-triangle* numbers, for instance?

◆ What about *symmetrical* numbers? This could mean palindromic (reading the same forwards and backwards) or refer to line symmetry or rotational symmetry when written in numerals. Which number is the most symmetrical number possible? What if you use Roman numerals instead of Arabic numerals?

◆ *Quick* numbers – which numbers are quickest to write? Or to say? Or to type on a qwerty keyboard?

◆   *Interesting* numbers – what is the smallest *un*interesting number? Whatever it is, doesn't it being the smallest uninteresting number make it in fact an *interesting* number?

A lot of energy can be created by this kind of thinking, leading to many lines to investigate. Work may touch on varied areas of mathematics. Perhaps more importantly, a sense that mathematics is alive and growing and changing can be very powerful. 'Polygon numbers', for instance, are not a new idea, yet if learners have not previously encountered them, constructing definitions can be a valuable experience even if the definitions are different from established ones.

Example 14.2 **Trigonometry**

Sometimes invention is unintentional, yet mistakes do often lead to interesting and worthwhile mathematical activity, and it is generally better to see *why* something is wrong than just to try not to think about it for fear of getting confused.

For example, a learner once said as he left a lesson that he found SOHCAHTOA easy to remember "because it has CAT in the middle" and he likes cats. This sounded perfectly harmless, and he had disappeared down the corridor before anyone realised that SOHCAHTOA *doesn't* have CAT in the middle! What he had been working with was 'SOHCATOAH'. This naturally led to examining whether this could ever be true/useful:

♦ SOH means $\sin x = \dfrac{opp}{hyp}$, and that is always true by definition for any right-angled triangle.

♦ CAT means $\cos x = \dfrac{adj}{\tan x}$.

♦ OAH would mean $opp = \dfrac{adj}{hyp}$.

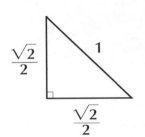

Both of these last two are dimensionally unsound, but, temporarily disregarding that, it is an interesting task to find triangles which satisfy one or both of the equations (e.g., the triangle on the left).

It won't be practical to try to pursue every loose end, but if such things are *never* looked into, something is lost, and a sense develops that 'other people's maths' is somehow always better than our own simply because of who made it rather than what it is.

Example 14.3 **Fractions and decimals**

Even when rules devised by learners have their limitations (which *all* rules do), they deserve serious consideration. Below is an alternative to the usual method for dividing fractions, and a way of remembering that multiplication by 100 is equivalent to division by 0.01.

Abby's Fractions Method:

To divide one fraction by another, 'sideways cancel' (if possible) and then multiply in an 'up-down-up' sense, shown by the arrows:

(The arrows conveniently make crosses with each other, illustrating 'multiplication'.)

$$\frac{2}{3} \div \frac{5}{7} = \frac{14}{15} \quad \boxed{\begin{array}{l} 2 \times 7 = 14 \\ 3 \times 5 = 15 \end{array}} \qquad \frac{3}{4} \div \frac{9}{16} = \frac{\cancel{3}^{1}}{\cancel{4}_{1}} \times \frac{\cancel{9}_{4}^{3}}{\cancel{16}} = \frac{4}{3}$$

Amy's Decimals Method:

When you divide a number by a number which is less than 1, it is the same as multiplying the number you have to divide by the number less than 1 read <u>backwards</u> missing out the decimal point. Eg. $\dfrac{2}{0.01}$ = 2 × 100 because you read 0.01 backwards so it is 100 (you must remember to miss out the decimal point).

When will these methods work? Will they ever go wrong? When? Why?

Bibliography

The following books can be extremely valuable sources of ideas and inspiration for teaching mathematics lessons.

ATM (1989) *Points of Departure 1-4*, ATM

Banwell, C., Saunders, K., Tahta, D. (1986) *Starting Points*, Tarquin

Bills, C., Bills, L., Watson, A. and Mason, J. (2004) *Thinkers*, ATM

Clausen-May, T. (2005) *Teaching Maths to Pupils with Different Learning Styles*, Paul Chapman Publishing

Ollerton, M. (2005) *100 Ideas for Teaching Mathematics*, Continuum

Ollerton, M. (2002) *Learning and Teaching Mathematics Without a Textbook*, ATM

Ollerton, M. and Watson, A. (2001) *Inclusive Mathematics 11-18*, Continuum

Mason, J. (1999) *Learning and Doing Mathematics*, QED

Mason, J. (2002) *Mathematics Teaching Practice: A guide for university and college lecturers*, Horwood

Watson, A. and Mason, J. (2005) *Mathematics as a Constructive Activity*, Lawrence Erlbaum

Watson, A. (2006) *Raising Achievement In Secondary Mathematics*, Open University

The following three books contain a lot of ideas (collected as well as original) for teaching specific mathematical topics:

Foster, C. (2003) *Instant Maths Ideas for Key Stage 3 Teachers: Number and Algebra*, Nelson Thornes

Foster, C. (2003) *Instant Maths Ideas for Key Stage 3 Teachers: Shape and Space*, Nelson Thornes

Foster, C. (2003) *Instant Maths Ideas for Key Stage 3 Teachers: Data, Numeracy and ICT*, Nelson Thornes

The following book contains rich and varied mathematics lessons:

Foster, C. (2008) *50 Mathematics Lessons*, Continuum

One of the best websites for stimulating learners' mathematical thinking is **http://nrich.maths.org/**.